Beyond the Horizon: A Remembrance Journal for Healing the
Loss of a Pet. In Honor of the Human-Animal Bond.

Juliann C. Corbin, Ph.D.

Beyond the Horizon: A Remembrance Journal for Healing the Loss of a Pet. In Honor of the Human-Animal Bond.

ISBN 978-1-7324044-0-3

Dedication
To Bridgit: My Forever Girl

Dear Bridgit,

The decade that was "you" had so many colors it makes a rainbow look dull. You filled all the nooks and crannies of my soul in the most peculiar way. I thought there would be no room for you in my broken heart but your insistent nature would have it no other way. You became a mirror to my own reflection and we came from the same spiritual cloth. Our era together was one of extreme highs and lows but together we managed to make our way through each difficult passage with even more vigor and strength. You showed me what it meant to be resilient as your physicality matched my own - literally step by step. In some way you held my pain and I yours, we became mirrors to each other. To see and experience the world through your eyes is a blessing that I will carry with me forever. Thank you for that gift Bridgit. This is one of the things I miss most about you; your unwavering determination to get to where you wanted and needed to be – my wellspring of eternal hope.

My memories of you so vivid and bountiful are woven into the tapestry of my being forever: In your puppy hood.... a bundle of untethered energy that knew no boundary. In your young adult years.... a focused and stubborn concentration, perhaps THE most beautiful Golden my eyes have ever seen. In your later years.... a bonding so deep and an understanding of the mystery that was you and I became crystal clear.

It is amazing how your 55 lbs. could fill up so much space; hence the nickname Biggs. At times you seemed bigger than life and somehow, I imagined that you would live on forever. However,

i

reality overtook magical thinking and it became clear that your time was near….Your food and water bowls are still in their spot but only now, every night, you dine by candlelight and water nourishes the Bodhi tree that has taken residence in your water bowl symbolizing your "awakening". Our final summer together, the summer of 2016, was the bell lap. Time was moving faster than we could keep stride with, so we kicked it into high gear and took in everything our senses and body allowed. I can still see your small but strong beautiful golden body in the water where you were most at home. I can still see your reflection on the water as if your soul has been imprinted on the ripples for eternity. With almost a sense of urgency you met the fall and winter as if it were both your first and last all contained in a single moment. I will never forget your last hike just 10 days before you passed. Something magical happened that day as you seemed to become one with the trail and rewound time to when your body was as free as your soul; perhaps this is how you now feel. In my mind's eye I can still see you so effortlessly charging up every hill with puppy like yet focused energy.

As the seasons come and go I am reminded of the impermanent nature of all life but most of all I am reminded that you live on in each breath I take, in each sunrise and sunset, in the warm breeze and the ripples on your favorite lake.

"I love you till before ever you were born" and you will always be my "forever girl". When I think of you Bridgit, I will bring to mind and spirit the joyful memories of the beautiful life we shared together. Rest in peace my sweet, sweet Bridgit until we are together again in fields of gold.

Love Forever, Mom
June 15, 2017

Preface

The need for a professionally written Journal on Pet Loss has several origins; personal, professional and research. My personal experience of the unique challenges encountered after the death of a beloved animal companion such as; limited communal support, lack of understanding and empathy, and lack of professional support made it clear that the clinical underpinnings of this phenomena is limited. Through my own struggles, I discovered firsthand the need for professional support services and resources.

Additionally, this journal is an outgrowth of my clinical work as a Doctor of Clinical Psychology and a Licensed Mental Health Professional. During my 20 years of clinical work with bereaved pet owners, I witnessed firsthand the difficulties experienced due to the lack of education, awareness and support in this overlooked area. When recommending adjunctive treatment modalities such as books and journals on Pet Loss there is only a limited selection with most written from a lay person/peer perspective that would not be suitable for my clients. Creating a professional Journal for healing the loss of a pet allows me to help bereaved pet owners beyond the confines of my therapy room, enabling me to reach a limitless number of people in need of such a resource.

Finally, my scholarly research on the Human -Animal Bond and Pet Loss entitled, *"A Phenomenological Study of Canine Loss and Grief Response: Clinical and Depth Psychological Implications"* *(2006),* points to a gap in resources and evidence-based treatment for those who experience the disenfranchised grief related to the death of a companion animal. Historically, the death of a companion animal has been compared to human loss. However, if you were to examine current theories on Pet Loss what they have in common is an attempt to explain the grief process from the vantage point of human loss without taking into consideration the disenfranchised nature and increases potential for complicated grief response. Because the bond we share with our companion animals is unique, complex and multifaceted as compared to any other bond we share, the experience of this loss has its own set of specific circumstances. This Journal approaches and understands the grief experienced by bereaved pet owners from this vantage point and offers a deep level of clinical, research and personal understanding of these dynamics.

This Journal is not a replacement for professional counseling or psychological care but rather a guide to facilitate your process and express, in written form, your emotions associated with the loss of your beloved companion animal. It is my belief that the emotional difficulty encountered by bereaved pet owners is best explained from a framework of professional knowledge of the grief response unique to pet loss. Offering a professionally written Pet Loss Journal is a necessary movement towards validating and giving significance to the Human-Animal Bond and subsequent grief experienced when this bond is broken through death or other means. May this journal bring you comfort and peace during this most difficult time.

Introduction

The death of a beloved pet is a very difficult and personal experience and you may find there are occasions when it can be too difficult to talk about your feelings. During these times it can be therapeutic to engage in Reflective Writing or Journal Therapy as this can be a helpful tool in attaining emotional clarity, validation and provides the means to help you develop a deeper understanding of your emotional process. This Pet Loss Journal offers a safe space for you to get in touch with and express your feelings and deepest emotions of losing your loved one.

This Journal begins with exploring the nature of the unique bond and relationship that you shared with your beloved pet throughout his or her lifetime. The Journal then moves on to the topic of Pet Bereavement. This is presented in specific sections designed to address the emotional and psychological process associated with the death of a companion animal. The first section provides general questions and prompts to help you explore emotions that may be on the surface but too difficult to retrieve. The second section provides a framework for you to explore some of your feelings and struggles unique to the marginalized and disenfranchised nature surrounding the death of your pet. The third and final section guides you through the stages common following the death of a companion animal and provides a guide for you to reflect on your subjective experiences, thoughts and feelings as they apply to your loss.

Just as there is no right or wrong way to grieve there is no right or wrong way to Journal. Use this Journal to create a healing and sacred space where you can openly express your thoughts and feelings of losing your beloved animal companion without judgement or shame. Allow yourself the time and space to reflect on your unique relationship and grieving process; sometimes you may want to engage in writing and other times you may just want to be mindful and be reflective in your thoughts. This Journal will allow you to reflect on your grieving process and how your experience changes over time as well as provide a "linkage" that serves to connects you to your beloved pet. It is my hope that you will find this journal to be an integral part of your journey towards wellness and healing.

Table of Contents

This Journal is in Loving Memory of:

Date of Birth:

Date of Arrival:

Date of Death:

"In a fractured world of broken relationships dogs can teach us the meaning of devotion and fidelity".
– Monks of New Skete

The Human Animal Bond: Reflections of our Relationship

The Human-Animal Bond: A General Overview

There are as many reasons to love our pets as there are stars in the sky with each relationship bringing something magical to that era of our lives. If you are fortunate enough to have experienced the unconditional love and devotion of a companion animal then you have also experienced the heartache of loss. To fully understand the emotional impact of suffering the loss of a companion animal, it is important to reflect on the dynamic and powerful bond we share with our pets.

The relationship with our pets encompasses some of the strongest bonds within human life; family member, daily companion, surrogate child, friend, mother, twin, and partner. Furthermore, this relationship embodies the essence of unconditional positive regard, trust, and safety which provides a wellspring of acceptance and support – something that is needed but not always found in human relationships. Because of the emotional closeness to, responsibility for, and activities shared with our companion animals, we naturally become emotionally dedicated and attached and of course grieve when they die.

Though many of us agree that pets often function as a substitute for human interaction, relationships with our pets are unique and serve many roles therefore should not be viewed simply as a mirror of human relationships. For example, companion animals can function as a transitional object in that they provide the framework for consistency and predictability in a world that, for some, be experienced as unstable and chaotic. In this sense, pets provide a secure base, give us a sense of stability, reliability, provide self-soothing/self-calming functions and emotional support during times of uncertainty and change. Unlike other relationships in our lives, pets become an emotional and psychological anchor in the midst of life transitions and crisis's. This aspect of the human-animal bond is significant for those who have experienced personal trauma, abuse or certain psychological conditions. In my clinical practice I have seen the positive therapeutic impact of the human-animal bond, especially with Emotional Support Animals in assisting those with mental health issues such as anxiety, panic depression, ADD, and PTSD.

In addition to the bonds individuals form with companion and Emotional Support Animals are the bonds disabled people form with service dogs and Veterans with PTSD trained dogs. Service dogs become the literal eyes, ears, hands and legs for those with disabilities which serves to further enhances the bond. PTSD Service dogs are trained to recognize, indicate and interrupt early signs of anxiety, panic attacks and nightmares enabling Veterans to break the cycle, redirect and regain emotional control. This serves to create a powerful relationship built on trust, safety and security.

Our pets also provide an enriched sense of the spiritual and a connection to nature. Until most recently (and for most of human history), humans have connected to nature on a daily basis in order to fulfill our inborn sensitivity and need for the natural world. Not surprising, our need for connecting with the natural world includes animals and our relationship to them. As our world becomes more urbanized, overpopulated and technology driven, person-to-person interaction and contact with the nature is less significant in everyday life. Social media has replaced "real time" friendships and the internet age will continue to facilitate this fundamental shift in interpersonal relations. People separating from one another leaves something missing - something core to our existence and our beloved pets fill this gap. Our intrinsic desire for love, closeness, and affiliation with nature draws so many of us to our pets, making that contact so extraordinary – especially in today's world!

While the discussion on the dynamic and diverse bond we share with our companion animals extends beyond the boundaries of this journal, the message here is that the **nature of your bond** and **degree of attachment** will certainly underscore the complexities inherent in your grieving process. Reflecting on your bond throughout the years allows you to remember the positive aspects and memories of your beloved pet - not just the pain of grieving. Additionally, many times people fear the memories of everyday life with their pet will begin to fade over time, so capturing this information while still fresh in your memory can offer an effective way to preserve your memories.

"The vulnerability present in the smallest of God's creatures calls out to our noblest instincts."
– Monks of New Skete

Our Bond: The Very Beginning

How and when I first met you and what my feelings, reactions, and first impressions were:

_____

_____

_____

_____

_____

_____

_____

The reason I wanted YOU and/or the reason you were chosen for me:

_____

_____

_____

_____

_____

_____

_____

_____

_____

_____

Your registered name, call name, birthday and date I brought you home:

_____

_____

_____

_____

Why I choose your name and the significance:

_____

_____

_____

_____

_____

My memories of how you looked, felt, smelled etc. when you were a puppy/kitten etc.:

_____

_____

_____

_____

_____

_____

_____

_____

When reflecting on our beginning together I can recall your unique and evolving personality as (describe characteristics that were central to your beloved pet):

_____

_____

_____

_____

_____

_____

_____

_____

_____

_____

As a puppy/kitten etc., your favorite activity, food, sleeping spot, toys were:

_____

_____

_____

_____

_____

_____

_____

_____

As a puppy/kitty etc. a typical morning/day/evening together would go something like this:

_____

_____

_____

_____

_____

_____

_____

_____

_____

_____

Some of our favorite places to visit when you were young were:

_____

_____

_____

_____

_____

_____

_____

_____

_____

_____

Things I learned from you and/or that you taught me about myself during our very beginning together:

_____

_____

_____

_____

_____

_____

_____

_____

_____

My fondest and happiest memories of you as a puppy/kitten etc. are:

_____

_____

_____

_____

_____

_____

_____

_____

_____

When I think of your very early years the things I miss most are:

_____

_____

_____

_____

_____

_____

_____

_____

_____

Reflecting on you as a puppy/kitten etc. brings about feelings of:

_____

_____

_____

_____

_____

_____

_____

_____

_____

_____

Reflections on our Bond and Relationship: The Beginning:

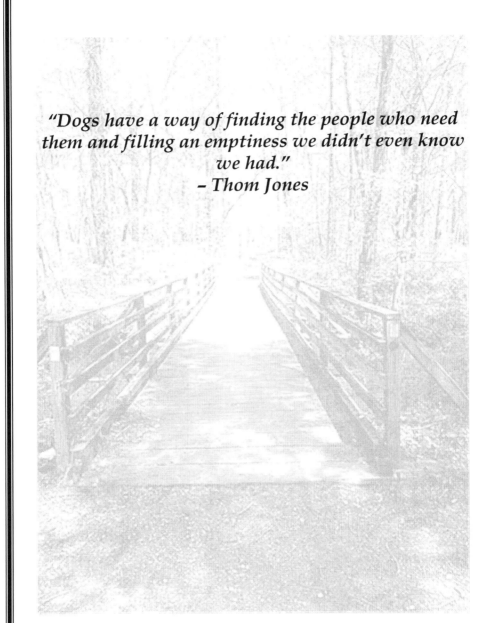

"Dogs have a way of finding the people who need them and filling an emptiness we didn't even know we had."
– Thom Jones

Our Bond: Your Adolescent Years

How our bond together grew in your adolescent years;
circumstances, challenges, that brought us closer together:

_____

_____

_____

_____

_____

_____

_____

_____

_____

_____

_____

_____

_____

_____

_____

_____

_____

_____

_____

14

The special activities we did together in your adolescent years that further cultivated our bond:

_____

_____

_____

_____

_____

_____

_____

_____

_____

As your distinctive personality began to unfold, you were appointed many nicknames. Some of my favorite nicknames for you and how they came about:

_____

_____

_____

_____

_____

_____

_____

_____

My memories of how you looked in your adolescent years:

_____

_____

_____

_____

_____

_____

_____

_____

When reflecting on your adolescent years this is how I recall your unique and evolving personality as (describe characteristics that were central to your beloved pet):

_____

_____

_____

_____

_____

_____

_____

_____

_____

_____

In your adolescent years your favorite food, sleeping spot and toys were:

_____

_____

_____

_____

_____

_____

_____

In your adolescent years, a typical morning/afternoon/evening together would look something like this:

_____

_____

_____

_____

_____

_____

_____

_____

_____

_____

In your adolescent years, some of your favorite activities and places to visit were:

_____

_____

_____

_____

_____

_____

_____

_____

Things I learned from you and/or that you taught me about myself in your adolescent years:

_____

_____

_____

_____

_____

_____

_____

_____

_____

What I miss most about our time together during your adolescent years and my happiest memories of you:

_____

_____

_____

_____

_____

_____

_____

_____

_____

_____

How you would greet me when I would return home after being away:

_____

_____

_____

_____

_____

_____

_____

Thinking of your adolescent years brings about feelings of:

_____

_____

_____

_____

_____

_____

_____

_____

_____

_____

_____

_____

_____

_____

_____

_____

_____

_____

_____

_____

Reflections on our Bond and Relationship: Your Adolescent Years

"If having a soul means being able to feel love and loyalty and gratitude, then animals are better off than a lot of humans."
- James Herriot

Our Bond: Your Adult Years

How our bond together continued to mature in your adult years; circumstances, challenges, events, that brought us closer together:

24

The special activities we did together in your adult years that further cultivated our maturing bond:

_____

_____

_____

_____

_____

_____

_____

_____

_____

How we would celebrate birthdays and holidays:

_____

_____

_____

_____

_____

_____

_____

_____

_____

My memories of how you looked in your adult years:

_____
_____
_____
_____
_____
_____
_____
_____
_____

When reflecting on your adult years, this is how I recall your
unique and evolving personality (describe characteristics that
were central to your beloved pet):

_____
_____
_____
_____
_____
_____
_____
_____
_____

In your adult years your favorite activities and places to visit were:

_____

_____

_____

_____

_____

_____

_____

_____

In your adult years your favorite food, sleeping spot and toys were:

_____

_____

_____

_____

_____

_____

_____

_____

_____

In your adult years a typical morning/afternoon/evening
together would look something like this:

_____

_____

_____

_____

_____

_____

_____

_____

_____

Things I learned from you and/or that you taught me about
myself in your adult years:

_____

_____

_____

_____

_____

_____

_____

_____

_____

What I miss most about our time together during your adult years:

_____

_____

_____

_____

_____

_____

_____

_____

My fondest and happiest memories of you as an adult are:

_____

_____

_____

_____

_____

_____

_____

_____

Reflecting on your adult years brings about feelings of:

_____

_____

_____

_____

_____

_____

_____

_____

_____

_____

_____

_____

_____

_____

_____

_____

_____

_____

_____

_____

_____

_____

Reflections on our Bond and Relationship: Your Adult Years:

31

"He is your friend, your partner, your defender, your dog. You are his life, his love, his leader. He will be yours faithful and true to the last beat of his heart. You owe it to him to be worthy of such devotion."
- Anonymous

33

Our Bond: Your Senior Years

How our bond continued to grow in your senior years;
circumstances, challenges and events that brought us closer
together:

_____

_____

_____

_____

_____

_____

_____

_____

_____

_____

_____

_____

_____

_____

_____

_____

_____

_____

Special activities we did together that continued to grow and strengthen our bond in your senior years:

_____

_____

_____

_____

_____

_____

_____

_____

_____

As you continued in your senior years the subtle and not so subtle changes I noticed:

_____

_____

_____

_____

_____

_____

_____

_____

_____

_____

Ways in which our routine began to change as you got older:

_____

_____

_____

_____

_____

_____

_____

_____

_____

My memories of how you looked in your senior years:

_____

_____

_____

_____

_____

_____

_____

_____

_____

When reflecting on your senior years I can recall your unique personality and defining features as (describe characteristics that were central to your beloved pet):

_____

_____

_____

_____

_____

_____

_____

_____

_____

In your senior years your favorite activity and places to visit were:

_____

_____

_____

_____

_____

_____

_____

_____

_____

In your senior years your favorite food, sleeping spot and toys were:

_____

_____

_____

_____

_____

_____

_____

In your senior years, a typical morning/afternoon/evening together would look something like this:

_____

_____

_____

_____

_____

_____

_____

_____

_____

_____

_____

Things I learned from you and / or that you taught me about myself in your senior years:

_____

_____

_____

_____

_____

_____

_____

_____

_____

What I miss most about our time together during your senior years:

_____

_____

_____

_____

_____

_____

_____

_____

_____

_____

My fondest and happiest memories of you in your senior years are:

_____

_____

_____

_____

_____

_____

_____

_____

_____

As I reflect on your senior years I feel:

_____

_____

_____

_____

_____

_____

_____

_____

_____

Reflections on our Bond and Relationship: Your Senior Years

"As I see your time is near, and the days of your youth have taken flight, every last breath I will spend by your side, I will not leave you to do this journey alone. Our time together seemed to be contained in that one final and last breath... one that I will remember for eternity. I will miss you my dear companion, for eternity I will miss you."
-Julianne Corbin

The End of Your Life

This is how I remember our final months, weeks and days together:

_____

_____

_____

_____

_____

_____

_____

_____

_____

_____

_____

_____

_____

_____

_____

_____

_____

_____

_____

_____

_____

Special "last time" events that we shared together and how I felt about it:

_____

_____

_____

_____

_____

_____

_____

_____

_____

_____

_____

_____

_____

_____

_____

_____

_____

_____

_____

_____

How you told me that it was ok and time to go or how I made that decision for you and what that was like:

_____

_____

_____

_____

_____

_____

_____

_____

_____

_____

_____

_____

_____

_____

_____

_____

_____

_____

_____

_____

_____

The circumstances around your final passage and how I felt and /or continue to feel about it (natural death, planned euthanasia, unexpected, at home, at veterinarian hospital):

_____

_____

_____

_____

_____

_____

_____

_____

_____

_____

_____

_____

_____

_____

_____

_____

_____

_____

_____

_____

_____

The reason I chose to be with you when you died or chose not to be with you and what that was like:

_____

_____

_____

_____

_____

_____

_____

_____

_____

_____

How I felt immediately after you passed:

_____

_____

_____

_____

_____

_____

_____

_____

_____

_____

Why I chose to be with your body after you died or why I chose not to and what it was like:

_____

_____

_____

_____

_____

_____

_____

_____

_____

How I chose to take care of your remains:

_____

_____

_____

_____

_____

_____

_____

_____

_____

Important items of yours that I placed with your body after you died and what they symbolized about you and our relationship:

_____

_____

_____

_____

_____

_____

_____

_____

_____

I did or did not have a memorial service to commemorate your life. If so this is where it was, what was done/said and who attended:

_____

_____

_____

_____

_____

_____

_____

_____

_____

Your final resting place and why this was chosen for you:

_____

_____

_____

_____

_____

_____

_____

This is how I chose to take care of your personal items (collar, toys, bed etc.):

_____

_____

_____

_____

_____

_____

_____

_____

_____

_____

_____

_____

Special items of yours that I have chosen to keep forever:

_____

_____

_____

_____

_____

_____

_____

_____

_____

Looking back on the" era" that was you, the role you played in my life and the needs you fulfilled can be best described as:

_____

_____

_____

_____

_____

_____

_____

_____

_____

Looking back over our time together, the eternal gifts you gave me are:

_____

_____

_____

_____

_____

_____

_____

_____

_____

This is how you kept me grounded and centered:

_____

_____

_____

_____

_____

_____

_____

_____

_____

_____

Some of the difficult things we went through together and how you helped me:

_____

_____

_____

_____

_____

_____

_____

_____

_____

How I helped you during difficult and challenging times:

_____

_____

_____

_____

_____

_____

_____

_____

_____

_____

The "would of", "should of", "could of" thoughts that go through my mind regarding the end of your life:

_____

_____

_____

_____

_____

_____

_____

_____

_____

Any regrets I have and why:

_____

_____

_____

_____

_____

_____

_____

_____

_____

_____

If I could change the ending of your life this is how it would look:

_____

_____

_____

_____

_____

_____

_____

_____

_____

_____

_____

_____

_____

_____

_____

_____

_____

_____

_____

_____

_____

_____

I did or did not write a Eulogy for you. If not why and if so this what it says:

_____

_____

_____

_____

_____

_____

_____

_____

_____

_____

_____

_____

_____

_____

_____

_____

_____

_____

_____

_____

_____

_____

_____

Reflections on the End of Your Life:

*"What we have enjoyed, we can never lose ...
all that we love deeply becomes a part of
us."*
- Helen Keller

Pet Bereavement: My Healing Journey Through Loss

Pet Bereavement: An Introduction

Simply speaking, grief is a universal and natural emotional reaction to the loss of someone close to us or a change of any kind, which of course includes the death of a beloved pet. While there are stages common to both human and pet loss, the lens from which we view the death of a pet needs to shift slightly in order to better understand the process. While it is natural to compare the loss of a pet to that of a human, the fact remains that the losses are indeed different! By saying the loss of a pet is different, I am not asserting that it is easier or more difficult (though for many people it may be), but rather has distinctive factors that form the grief reaction. As discussed earlier, factors such as but not limited to the **multifaceted nature of the bond** and the **disenfranchised nature of the loss** lends itself to the difficulties unique to the death of a pet.

While we do know that grieving follows general stages, the timing and experience of these stages are unique to the individual. Many times, people begin to "pathologize" themselves if they feel they are stuck in one stage too long or bounce back and forth between stages. It is imperative to remember that there is no pre-determined time line for the grieving process and it can be a long and difficult process. Additionally, grieving is not a linear process and it is natural (if not expected) to move back and forth from one stage to another or to feel a sense of permeability between stages - especially early on after the loss. A full discussion on Pet Loss is beyond the scope of this journal, however, following are a few FAQ's that have been asked by my clients over the years. It is my hope that these keys points help to answer some of your questions and provide a framework for your experience.

Frequently Asked Questions:

1. **Are there "stages" of pet loss and are they similar to that of human loss?** Yes, there are definitive stages or phases that the bereaved go through after the death of a pet and do share characteristic of human loss. Based on my years of clinical work with bereaved pet owners and as highlighted in my research on the Human-Animal Bond (2006) these stages follow a general non- linear pattern of:
   - Shock and Disbelief
   - Painful Emotions
   - Living in the Past
   - Acceptance and Reconciliation

As noted earlier, while the stages of pet loss share similarities to that of human loss, variables such as the disenfranchised nature of the loss, the role pets play in our lives and the nature of the relationship can all have a direct impact on the way we experience our grief. For some, these factors can result in a complicated and prolonged grief response not always experienced in human loss.

2. **How long will it take to "get over" the death of my pet?** I do not like to use the word "get over"– a cold is something we get over, not the death of a beloved pet. The reality is you will not 'get over' the loss of a loved one; you will learn to live with their absence. You will heal and you will rebuild yourself around the loss you have suffered. The time frame for integration and reconciliation varies from individual to individual. Variables such as; the age of your pet, circumstances involving the death, the nature of your bond and connection, your emotional constitution and support system all play a role in how long it will take to process your grief. It is important to recognize that grief is not always a linear process and you may find yourself moving back and forth from one stage to another. While some people can begin feeling better in 6-8 months, others

take much longer. **Generally** speaking, if your grief symptoms have not subsided in 12 months or at any time you feel suicidal it is recommended that you seek the help of a trained professional.

3. **I never thought the death of my pet would be this painful! Is this normal?** I have had many clients share that they felt more grief over the loss of their pet then the loss of some family members. This tends to create intense feelings of guilt and despair. It is important to remember it is not **what** we have lost, but rather the **nature and degree** of the attachment, connection, depth of love and meaning that our loved one had in our lives that defines our process. Despite what some people may think, it is completely normal to feel intense grief after the death of your beloved pet. It is important that you find people and resources that will serve to validate your loss. In addition, many times the loss of a pet can trigger and bring to surface unresolved losses of the past.

4. **I know she/he was a pet but I loved them like my own child and no one seems to understand. Is there something wrong with me?** No, your ability to love so deeply is not "wrong". For certain people a pet can be the "object" by which maternal and paternal impulses and instincts are projected onto, especially those without human children. In this sense, yes, your pet can take on a similar emotional and psychological role in your life that a child would. It is important to honor that your relationship was extremely deep and meaningful and not to judge yourself for the bond you had with your pet.

5. **When is the right time to get another pet?** There is no definitive answer to this question. It is important to remember that pets are not replaceable or interchangeable. Many times, people will impulsively rush to get another pet to avoid the grieving process. This is not only unfair to

the new pet as it will not live up to the expectations of the owner, but also does a disservice to the bereaved by not allowing the space and time to properly grieve. On the other hand, I have had clients who report that getting a new pet was the only thing that helped them with their grieving process. Every person is different and only you will know when the time is right. One thing I say to my clients is if you wait till you no longer miss your deceased pet to get another, you may never get a new one since there will always be a part of you that misses your beloved. Being in an emotional space where you can continue to be present to your grieving process, while at the same time open your heart and home to a new family member is when the time is right.

6. **Can one experience grief when the loss is unrelated to death?** The "loss" of a pet can take on many forms and one need not die in order to feel grief. For example, if your pet gets lost or if you are forced to give up your pet due to relocation or declining health are situations that can bring on an intense grief response. Our lives are filled with many necessary losses that do not include death. Watching our once young and vibrant pet grow old reminds us that (most likely) we will outlive them and this can trigger emotional distress. It is very difficult to watch someone we love grow old and while this is the natural course of life, it can trigger our own issues surrounding death, dying and mortality.

"The reality is that you will grieve forever. You will not 'get over' the loss of a loved one; you will learn to live with it. You will heal and you will rebuild yourself around the loss you have suffered. You will be whole again but you will never be the same."
-Elisabeth Kubler-Ross

General Pet Bereavement Questions

Sometimes it's hard to know where to begin the process of journaling as feelings associated with loss are not always clear and we do not know exactly where or how to begin. Following are some prompts and questions I use as a starting point to help my clients get in touch with their feelings associated with their loss. Some prompts are general and some more specific. You may find you resonate to some questions more than others, so focus on the questions that seem most important and meaningful to you. Remember there is no "right" or "wrong way to journal!

I remember when....

_____

_____

_____

_____

_____

_____

_____

_____

_____

The first time I _ and what that was like for me:

_____

_____

_____

_____

_____

_____

_____

_____

_____

_____

_____

What I recall and felt in those first hours and days after you died:

_____

_____

_____

_____

_____

_____

_____

_____

What I recall and felt in first weeks after you died:

_____

_____

_____

_____

_____

_____

_____

_____

_____

If applicable, what I recall and felt on the first year anniversary of your death:

_____

_____

_____

_____

_____

_____

_____

_____

_____

_____

The most difficult lessons I have learned since your passing are:

_____

_____

_____

_____

_____

_____

_____

_____

_____

The greatest lesson I have learned since your passing is:

_____

_____

_____

_____

_____

_____

_____

_____

_____

How I felt the first time I visited one of our favorite places:

_____

_____

_____

_____

_____

_____

_____

_____

_____

_____

Some healthy and not so healthy ways I express my grief:

_____
_____
_____
_____
_____
_____
_____
_____
_____
_____

Some of ways that I hold in my grief:

_____
_____
_____
_____
_____
_____
_____
_____
_____
_____
_____
_____

How I would describe my process thus far:

_____

_____

_____

_____

_____

_____

_____

_____

_____

Words that best describe how I feel today:

_____

_____

_____

_____

_____

_____

_____

_____

_____

_____

How it felt on "first anniversary" dates such as: your birthday, holidays, change of seasons etc.:

_____

_____

_____

_____

_____

_____

_____

_____

_____

My happiest memory of you is and why:

_____

_____

_____

_____

_____

_____

_____

_____

This is what I want or need to say to you:

_____

_____

_____

_____

_____

_____

_____

_____

_____

_____

_____

_____

_____

_____

_____

_____

_____

_____

_____

_____

_____

_____

Additional Reflections:

"My grief is no less because you think it should be."
– Author Unknown

Pet Loss and Disenfranchised Grief

What is disenfranchised grief and why is the loss of beloved pet considered disenfranchised? Disenfranchised grief is any type of loss that is not acknowledged by society as being significant and the type of grief that is experienced when a loss cannot be openly acknowledged, socially sanctioned, or publicly mourned. The death of a companion animal falls under the category of a disenfranchised loss because;

- The *relationship* between humans and their pet is not always acknowledged and recognized by society as being relevant or significant (though there is a collective shift towards that end) and there is a false assumption that closeness and love can exist and thrive only between humans. This results in the bereaved pet owner being cut off from societal supports typically available after human loss. Individuals who do not understand the unique bond between a human and animal fail to realize the emotional, psychological and spiritual bonding that often occurs and what it is like for the bereaved when those bonds are broken through death. Because of this, the grieving process becomes minimized by others which may result in the bereaved feeling a sense of shame when expressing their grief. We have all heard the well- meaning yet hurtful statement, "it was just a dog /cat" or "just go get another one" in response to the loss of a pet. This failure by family and friends to recognize the relationship between a human and pet as being worthy of grieving leads to marginalizing and isolating the bereaved pet owner from support networks available after human loss.
- Because the *loss* of a companion animal is not always recognized as being worthy of grieving, it becomes trivialized by others. The lack of empathy and validation leads to a sense of embarrassment about expressing grief which can result in the bereaved suppressing their

emotions and engaging in isolating and maladaptive behaviors as a way to cope. Because of the disenfranchised nature of pet loss, the bereaved have fewer opportunities to openly express and resolve them with friends, family and the community. This leaves many bereaved pet owners feeling alienated from their community and resources, which lends itself to an increase risk for emotional and psychological difficulties such as depression, PTSD and complicated grief (Corbin, 2006).

- For the *bereaved* pet owner, there is no formality in memorializing their deceased pet or opportunity to publicly mourn the loss of their beloved pet. Because of the disenfranchised nature of the death of a pet, many bereaved pet owners do not engage in memorial services typical after human loss. A funeral service is an expression of affection and gratitude to the deceased, however, when our pet dies, there is no formal or public rituals whereby we can express and share sorrow, talk about the loss or get the sympathy and support of others. The healing aspect of memorializing (providing emotional comfort, concretizing the loss, and assisting in facilitating the grief process) are denied to the bereaved pet owner. This lack of formal ritual can have serious consequences on the bereaved's ability to accept the finality of the death, serves to further marginalize bereaved pet owners, and creates a sense of isolation and aloneness that may not be experienced during human loss.

For those who have been fortunate enough not to experience the disenfranchised aspect of pet loss the following section may not be relevant. For others, the following questions and reflections help guide you towards re-enfranchising your loss by identifying and expressing your feelings about your experience of disenfranchised loss and will help you gain a deeper understanding of how the marginalized loss of your beloved pet has informed your grieving process. This section will assist in validating your loss by helping you recognize that your loss and associated feelings are normal, relevant and important!

Since you died, I find that sometimes (or all the time!) I feel as if I do not have the right or am not entitled to grieve. The reasons that I feel this way and how this makes me feel:

_____

_____

_____

_____

_____

_____

_____

_____

_____

Since you died, I feel like there is something wrong with me because of how I deeply I miss you. I feel this way because:

_____

_____

_____

_____

_____

_____

_____

_____

_____

Knowing that my pain reflects how much I love and miss you, I will begin to honor you and our relationship by:

_____

_____

_____

_____

_____

_____

_____

_____

_____

Regardless of how others have supported or not supported me, I must actively work towards acknowledging that my love for you is true, significant and your loss no less valid then human loss (s). Some mantra's and supportive statements that I can repeat to myself in difficult times are:

_____

_____

_____

_____

_____

_____

_____

_____

Sometimes I feel as though your death is not worthy of time and space to grieve. I feel this way because:

_____

_____

_____

_____

_____

_____

_____

_____

_____

I must actively and mindfully remind myself that I am worthy of grieving and that my grief is important. I give myself permission to grieve. Ways that I can be mindful of my mourning process are:

_____

_____

_____

_____

_____

_____

_____

_____

Although at times I feel very alone, perhaps if I look around me there are supports in places I have never thought of. Some of these places or people might be:

_____

_____

_____

_____

_____

_____

_____

_____

_____

_____

Even though I wanted to, I felt that it was not "acceptable" for me to engage in a ritual or memorial to honor your life and passing. Knowing it IS healthy and natural this is how I can see having a memorial in your honor:

_____

_____

_____

_____

_____

_____

_____

Knowing that my grief is a testament of my love and devotion to you, I give myself permission to explore my grief and express my emotions in a way that is unique to our relationship and personal to me. Some ways that I can see doing this are:

_____

_____

_____

_____

_____

_____

_____

_____

_____

_____

_____

_____

_____

_____

_____

_____

_____

_____

_____

_____

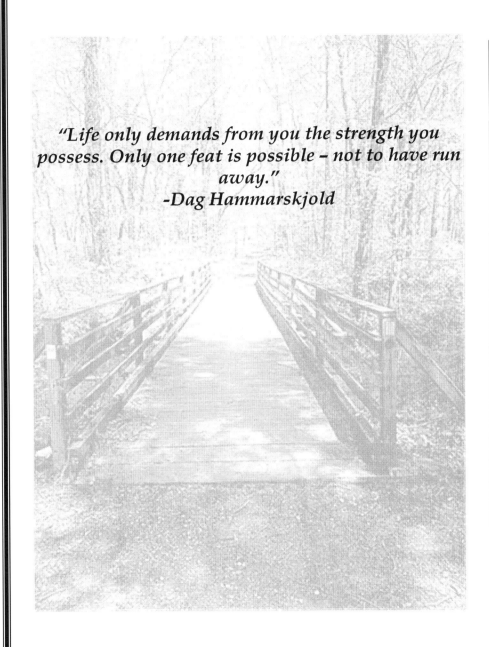

"Life only demands from you the strength you possess. Only one feat is possible – not to have run away."
-Dag Hammarskjold

The Healing Journey:
Stages of Grief

Shock and Disbelief

In the days, weeks or months following the death of a beloved companion animal, it is common to experience shock and disbelief: a sort of emotional anesthesia. Just as our bodies can experience physical shock in response to pain, so can our psyche experience psychological shock in the wake of emotional trauma such as after the death of a loved one. This is very normal and can be thought of as a coping mechanism to help deal with emotions that are too overwhelming and our way to repress the shocking reality that is too difficult to process at that time. During this stage, it is common for bereaved pet owners to experience; emotional numbness, feeling emotionally "frozen", denial, repression of painful emotions, dissociative features such as observing what is going on from afar and being in a "fog". Some bereaved pet owners also find themselves engaging in searching and calling out behaviors during this stage. Because some people might mistake shock and disbelief as lack of caring or feeling, it is important to note that emotional numbness is a protective response to the trauma that will lessen over time.

While there are things you can actively do to support your process, you should not attempt to push the natural course of grieving. It can be counterproductive to attempt to force yourself out of this stage too soon since doing so may reinforce the natural defenses already in place. There is no predetermined time frame for the grieving process, there will be many ebbs and flows and grieving does not occur in a linear fashion. When the time is right, you will eventually begin to acknowledge the reality of the loss. The grieving process truly begins when you move from a place of shock and disbelief to one of acknowledging the reality of the death. The grieving process is very delicate and needs to be respected and honored in a way that allows for an organic unfolding towards reconciliation. As you begin to move out of shock and disbelief, it is helpful to have "linking objects" that remind you of your special bond and help you to feel a sense of closeness to your deceased pet. With that in mind, below are some suggestions to help gently ease and guide your way through this stage:

- Find a "safe" friend (s) that understand your pain and that you are comfortable talking to about the loss. Since at this very early stage you are feeling a sense of numbness, you may not necessarily talk about your feelings but talking about the death and circumstances surrounding the loss can be helpful.
- You may find that you need to repeat the details of the death over and over. This is okay and very natural as this helps to concretize the trauma and bring a sense of reality to the loss. Recite and recount what has been lost as often as you need.
- Don't pretend things are okay when clearly things are anything but! Be honest with yourself and others regarding your feelings or lack thereof.
- Eventually you will be able to face the reality of "death" squarely in the face by calling it what it is. Challenge yourself to name it, spell it etc.
- Gently and slowly confront reminders as opposed to avoiding them. This includes things like people and situations that you associate with your deceased pet, look at old photos and videos, visit the grave, view the ashes visit special places you have gone to together, touch toys, blankets, and other belongings.
- Create and surround yourself with "linking objects" during this time. These are items of your deceased pet that help to remind you and create a sense of closeness to them. Having these "linking objects" close by can assist in providing a sense of comfort which can lend itself to gently merging out of the shock and denial phase.

On the following page, you will find some questions to help you process through and gain insight into this stage of your grieving process.

When I think of the days and week right after you passed some of the things I experienced were:

- denial
- repression of painful feelings
- dissociation
- emotional numbness
- feelings of derealization
- feelings of depersonalization

How I felt in the days and weeks after you died:

_____

_____

_____

_____

_____

_____

_____

_____

_____

_____

_____

_____

_____

_____

_____

Friends or family members that were most supportive following your death and how they helped me:

_____

_____

_____

_____

_____

_____

_____

_____

The people, places and situations that I associate with you and places I avoid are:

_____

_____

_____

_____

_____

_____

_____

_____

The first time I viewed your ashes or visited your grave and how it felt for me:

_____

_____

_____

_____

_____

_____

_____

_____

_____

Some of the things I did in the days and weeks following your death that helped to make me feel close to you:

_____

_____

_____

_____

_____

_____

_____

_____

_____

Some of the things I did in the days and weeks following your death that served to help me "forget":

_____

_____

_____

_____

_____

_____

_____

_____

_____

Some of the things I did to help comfort and take care of myself in the days and weeks after you passed:

_____

_____

_____

_____

_____

_____

_____

_____

In the days and weeks after you past, I found myself calling out and searching for you even though I knew you were gone. Some of my calling and searching out behaviors and the purpose they served were:

_____

_____

_____

_____

_____

_____

_____

As I work towards being able to acknowledge the reality of your death I feel:

_____

_____

_____

_____

_____

_____

_____

_____

_____

Reflections on Shock and Disbelief:

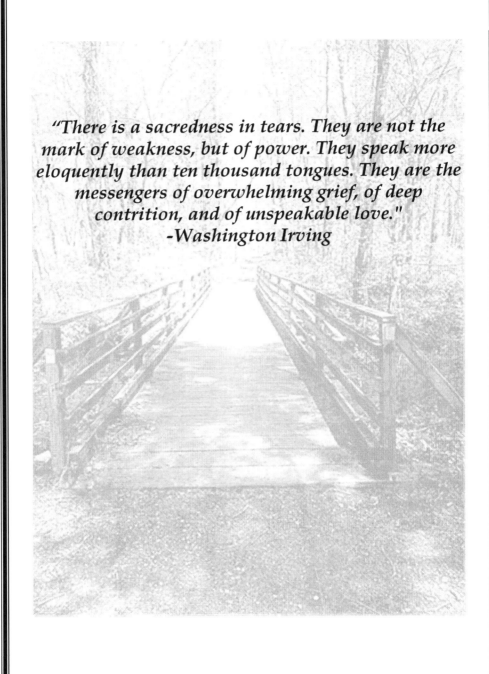

"There is a sacredness in tears. They are not the mark of weakness, but of power. They speak more eloquently than ten thousand tongues. They are the messengers of overwhelming grief, of deep contrition, and of unspeakable love."
-Washington Irving

Painful Emotions

As touched on previously, you may find yourself in a state of shock and disbelief as a means to defend against painful emotions. However, at such time when shock and disbelief begin to fade, it is common to begin to feel an emergence of painful emotions. During the painful emotions phase of grieving, you begin to better understand and acknowledge the permanency of the death. You may begin to experience emotions such as; anger, depression, guilt, sadness, fear, anxiety, lowered self-esteem, helplessness, irritability, and grief pangs. Counterfactual thinking such as "what if'" and "if only" is normal during this stage as you begin to wonder if you could have changed the outcome. As mentioned above depressive symptoms are very common and can include:

- constant sadness, anxiety, or feelings of emptiness
- feelings of guilt or helplessness
- loss of interest in hobbies
- insomnia or oversleeping
- physical aches that don't go away with treatment
- suicidal thoughts or suicide attempts
- hopelessness
- changes in appetite
- lack of interest in daily activities
- sleep disturbances

Grief pangs are also common and are experienced as waves of sudden and very intense feelings of emotional distress. They are referred to as "waves" because of the strong and unpredictable nature of them. While grief pangs can feel overwhelming, they are part of the normal grieving process, especially in the beginning. Episodes of grief pangs can occur spontaneously, however, many things can trigger a grief pang such as;

- Finding a piece your pet's fur.
- Seeing or touching your pet's toys or other belongings.
- Finding an old photograph.
- Waking up and finding your pet is not beside you.
- Meeting someone you haven't seen for a while who asks about your pet or how you are.
- Going to places that you associate with your pet.
- A special song or scent that reminds you of your pet.

It is not uncommon to experience physical symptoms as a normal part of the grieving process. These symptoms may be primary or secondary to anxiety. Some of these may include:

- hollowness in stomach
- nausea
- tightness in chest or throat
- breathlessness
- muscle weakness
- lightheaded
- fatigue
- weight change
- heart palpitations
- sighing
- headaches
- restlessness
- dizziness
- headaches

Following are some suggestions to help work through the painful emotions of losing a beloved companion animal:

- Allow yourself to experience the painful emotions of the loss: As difficult as it can be, grief is a natural and healthy reaction to the loss of someone we love – be it human or animal. As touched on earlier, bereaved pet owners may feel guilty and not entitled to grieve but keeping your feelings in is unhealthy and can lead to maladaptive coping strategies. It is commonplace to assume we should naturally "get over" the loss and "move on", but this view is not a realistic way to think about grief. It is essential to allow yourself the time and space to grieve and experience the emotions of grief, such as shock, sadness, anger, depression etc. Do not minimize your situation or judge yourself for having these feelings. Allow yourself to react in ways authentic to you and which help you process and release powerful emotions (even if it means screaming or crying or punching a pillow!). For some it may be necessary to set aside quiet time every day to reflect on your beloved companion animal and give yourself permission to experience any emotions that come up without judgement.

- Talk with others: Choose a few friends or family members that understand what you are going through and be transparent with them about your feelings. Sharing what you are going through with others may help you concretize, process and release your feelings. Let your friends and family know it is important for you to share your feelings with them and that you are not looking for them to "fix" things but just need them to listen. Verbally re-living the experience is a useful technique to come to terms with the reality of the loss and your emotions, especially guilt when euthanasia is involved. You may find you need to tell and re-tell your story over and over again - this is normal and to be expected.

- Find Creative Outlets for Active Grieving: There may be occasions when you just do not feel like talking. Sometimes it can be challenging to find words for what we are going through and as a result our emotions can stay inside of us with no means for expression. During these times it is helpful to be "active" with your feelings as the act of creating following a death can be especially cathartic. Consider expressing your feelings through creative activities such as: music, art, dance, writing, photography, cooking, painting, etc. Writing your thoughts and feelings in a journal can be useful as it provides a safe and private outlet for your feelings and provides a link to your beloved pet.

- Engage in Physical Activity: Find a physical activity such as swimming, walking, hiking, running, or riding a bicycle to help you cope with your feelings. Exercise and activities like hitting a punching bag or hitting golf balls at a driving range may help release frustration or anger. Exercise releases powerful chemicals in our brain such as endorphins, serotonin and BDNF (Brain Derived Neurotropic Factor). These chemicals can be helpful in coping with grief as they decrease the stress response, decrease depressive symptoms and can enhance mood.

- Give Yourself a Respite from Grieving: We all need a break! It may be necessary to consciously set time aside every day to take time away from grieving. Whether it is a bath, shower or a trip to the store be sure to practice mindfulness of being fully "in" the activity. Consider practicing daily meditation as this is an excellent way to calm the mind, relax the body and instill a sense of inner peace.

- Keep a routine: Cultivating a basic routine of everyday activities serves to structure your time and keeps you connected to familiar people and places. This also helps you cultivate a sense of normalcy during a time when things are anything but normal for you.

- Be patient and allow your grief to unfold at a pace natural for you. Try not to judge or criticize yourself for not coping as well or healing as quickly as you think you "should". Everyone needs to grieve in a manner and pace that is right for him or her.

- Join a Pet Loss support group or online support: Both in person and online Pet Loss support groups can provide the opportunity to speak with others who are going through similar struggles. Group members can provide encouragement, comfort, guidance, understanding and can help to normalize your experience and reassure you that you are not alone in your grief!

Following are questions to help you process some of your painful emotions surrounding the death of your beloved pet.

As my shock and disbelief begins to dissipate some of the emotions I feel are:

_____

_____

_____

_____

_____

_____

_____

_____

_____

The emotions that are the most predominate and difficult for me are and why:

_____

_____

_____

_____

_____

_____

_____

_____

_____

Some of the ways I express these difficult emotions are:

_____

_____

_____

_____

_____

_____

_____

Some healthy coping techniques I engage in to help process my painful emotions are:

_____

_____

_____

_____

_____

_____

_____

_____

_____

_____

_____

Some of the not so healthy coping techniques I engage in to help process my painful emotions are:

_____

_____

_____

_____

_____

_____

_____

_____

At times, I find myself trying to hide my true feelings to myself and others. The reason I do this and how this makes me feel:

_____

_____

_____

_____

_____

_____

_____

_____

_____

I sometimes find myself engaging in "if only" and "what if" counterfactual thinking. If I were to re-frame these thoughts into a more balance view it would look something like this:

_____

_____

_____

_____

_____

_____

_____

_____

As my painful emotions begin to subside or shift, I feel (relief, guilt etc.):

_____

_____

_____

_____

_____

_____

_____

_____

Reflections on Painful Emotions:

"Life is eternal, and love is immortal, and death is only a horizon; and a horizon is nothing save the limit of our sight."
- Rossiter Worthington Raymond

Living in the Past

A common experience I have discovered in both my clinical work and scholarly research is the tendency for bereaved pet owners to live in or stay in the past. Living in the past is often times experienced as; a sense of ambivalence towards the future, resistant to change, lack of desire to engage in new activities and a need to engage in the same activities and patterns as when the pet was still alive. Living in the past is an outgrowth of painful feelings as the connection to your companion animal is preserved through engagement in these familiar emotions and patterns. In this sense, the experience of living in the past serves to link you to your pet and the concept of "moving on" is often met with resistant. As mentioned by one of my research participants (Corbin, 2006), "Staying in my old pattern of doing things was the only thing that kept me connected to Sunny and people around me tried to take that away from me. People did not understand that I needed to stay close to all of her things and maintain my previous way of being because that was the only thing I had left of her. Beginning a new life in a world without her was not tolerable, so I stayed in the past – for a while anyway....

As highlighted above, during this stage, it can be challenging to re-engage in life and is common to focus on a time when your pet was alive and well. This is normal and to be expected. During this stage of grief, you may feel guilty doing things without your pet and have the desire to withdraw from people and activities. While still struggling with the loss, you may also feel the need to carry on with "normal" activities. This polarization can be the source of tension and conflict and it is normal to feel a sense of ambivalence from experiencing conflicting emotions at the same time. i.e. the inclination to continue on and re-engage in your life vs. the desire to stay in the past.

If not done so already, a task at this stage is to find a meaningful way to commemorate the death and memorialize the love you have for your beloved companion animal. Ritual and ceremony are the most common universal practices to memorialize the death of someone we love and can be valuable when there is an extreme burden of guilt or remorse about the death. Ceremony serves to draw the death into the present encouraging you to be more aware of the here and now and can be helpful for those who are having a difficult time re-engaging in life without their cherished companion animal. In this sense the commemoration serves to bring the death into the present rather than living in the past, thus helping you to live more fully in the present. Some ideas to commemorate the death of your companion animal are listed below:

- Hold a memorial service at a place special to your beloved pet where a poem, prayer or eulogy can be read.
- Plant a tree, bush, and/or create a memory garden of your beloved pet with a memorial stone.
- Donate money to a cause or charity that has significance to your beloved pet.
- If cremated, sprinkle your pet's ashes in a special place.
- Place a candle in the food bowl and light it during feeding times.
- Place an indoor plant in your pet's water bowl to symbolize your continued love.
- Create a memorial photo album or scrape book.
- Create a special box with items belonging to your beloved pet.
- Have a piece of jewelry made from your pet's ashes or photo.
- Volunteer at a Shelter to honor your pet's memory. By helping those in need your pet continues to have a positive impact on the lives of those less fortunate.
- Create keychain from your pet's tag as this was probably one of the first items you purchased for him or her.

Although these memorializing ideas are quite simple, their function is to create an avenue by which the memory you have and love you continue to feel is offered expression in the here and now.

Following are some questions to help you reflect and process through this stage:

Daily patterns that remain the same since you died:

_____

_____

_____

_____

_____

_____

_____

Daily patterns that have changed since you died and how this feels for me:

_____

_____

_____

_____

_____

_____

_____

_____

_____

_____

_____

_____

_____

_____

When I go to places that were special to us it makes me feel:

_____

_____

_____

_____

_____

_____

_____

_____

As time passes on, some of the ways that I resist change are:

_____

_____

_____

_____

_____

_____

_____

_____

_____

_____

As time passes on, some ways that I embrace change are:

_____

_____

_____

_____

_____

_____

_____

_____

_____

Finding a balance between my life when you were alive and my life without you here can best be described as:

_____

_____

_____

_____

_____

_____

_____

_____

_____

_____

The idea of relinquishing some of the past and integrating new roles into my life brings about feelings of:

_____

_____

_____

_____

_____

_____

_____

_____

_____

Life without you here is like:

_____

_____

_____

_____

_____

_____

_____

_____

_____

116

Reflections on Living in the Past:

"There is a land of the living and a land of the dead, and the bridge is love, the only survival, the only meaning."
-Thornton Wilder, The Bridge of San Luis Rey

Acceptance and Reconciliation

As you move through the trials and tribulations inherent in the grieving process, you may eventually find yourself in the stage of acceptance and reconciliation. Acceptance is the point when you can embrace the inevitability and permanency of the death of your companion animal and reconciliation is the adaptation process of becoming accustomed to an environment and life without your pet. This takes place as you work to integrate the new reality of moving forward and re-engaging in life without the physical presence of your beloved pet. At this stage you are able to make sense of what happened and reinvest energy in new ways. The loss no longer consumes the entirety of your emotional energy and you become available to pursue new activities and relationships. It is significant to mention that acceptance and reconciliation does not imply forgetting about or leaving your pet behind. Rather, it is the process of coming to a place whereby you have internalized and embodied the memory of your companion animal, enabling you to keep their essence forever present in your heart and evolving life.

We often think about the death of a loved one as something we are expected to "get over" in a predetermined amount of time, however, in reality this could not be further from the truth. As an alternative to thinking about the death of a loved one as something you are to eventually "getting over", reframe your thoughts in such a way that supports the idea of slowly adapting to life without the daily reminder of your beloved's physical presence. The idea that "time heals all" is not always true especially in the case of grief. It is not so much the passage of time that leads to healing but rather what you do in that time and how you engage with your grieving process that determines how you come to a place of acceptance and reconciliation. Acceptance does not ignore the loss but rather embraces the new reality and the point in the grieving process whereby responsibility and ownership of one's life and actions take on new meaning structures. Keep in mind, death ends a life not a relationship and allow your memories and continued love to sustain the beautiful bond you shared with your pet. Embrace the idea of forming a new relationship to and with your deceased pet - your love can forever continue on in the form of a living love. Become those very things that you most admired about your beloved pet and pay tribute to them every day!

Acceptance and Reconciliation may include the following:

- earlier painful feelings diminish in their intensity.
- ability to think of your deceased companion animal with less emotional and psychological suffering.
- ability to acknowledge and accept the complete reality of the death.
- capacity to talk about your companion animal without overwhelming emotions.
- a willingness to re-engage in life and form new meaning structures and relationships.
- move from living in the past to living in the present, marked by an investment in the future.
- begin to re-engage in daily living and new activities that did not involve your companion animal.
- restored ambivalence and the ability to experience life without your pet.
- formation of a different relation to and with your companion animal; an internalization of the love that is now a part of your subjective emotional world.
- you no longer feel guilty experiencing moments of happiness.
- you may consider bringing in a new pet to your household.

Some of the ways that I continue to keep you present in my life are:

_____

_____

_____

_____

_____

_____

_____

_____

_____

How my life has changed since you died and how I feel about these changes:

_____

_____

_____

_____

_____

_____

_____

_____

Some of the ways that I have changed since you died and how I feel about that:

_____

_____

_____

_____

_____

_____

_____

_____

_____

Ways that I continue to keep your memory alive in my life:

_____

_____

_____

_____

_____

_____

_____

_____

_____

_____

Some of the ways that you continue to inform my life and how our relationship continues on - even in your physical absence:

_____

_____

_____

_____

_____

_____

_____

_____

As I walk through my life I know it is healthy and natural to continue to keep the memory of you alive in my life. Some ways that I do this are:

_____

_____

_____

_____

_____

_____

_____

_____

If you were here right now this is what I would say to you:

_____

_____

_____

_____

_____

_____

_____

_____

_____

_____

_____

_____

_____

_____

_____

_____

_____

_____

_____

_____

_____

_____

_____

_____

Five words that best describe my experience of having known and loved you:

1.

2.

3.

4.

5.

Five words that best describe my experience of losing you:

1.

2.

3.

4.

5.

As I continue to make an effort to re-engage in life without your physical presence, I can internalize and embody the things that you symbolized in your life and through your death. I create this living memory of you by:

_____

_____

_____

_____

_____

_____

_____

_____

_____

_____

_____

_____

_____

_____

_____

_____

_____

_____

_____

Reflections on Reconciliation and Acceptance:

My Tribute Letter to You:

About Dr. Corbin

I am a New Jersey State Licensed Professional Counselor, Certified Clinical Counselor and Psychotherapist with 20 years of experience working in the field of grief to include; complicated grief, disenfranchised loss, traumatic loss, hospice counseling and end-of-life issues. I earned my Bachelor's Degree in Psychology from Temple University, my Master's Degree in Counseling Psychology from Chestnut Hill College and a Ph.D. in Clinical Psychology from Pacifica Graduate Institute

My lifelong love and passion for the Human-Animal Bond coupled with the lack of support I have seen professionally and experienced personally over the years for bereaved pet owners led me to specialize in Pet Bereavement counseling. As a Pet Breavement specialist and Licensed Mental Health Professional, I provide individual and group counseling services to bereaved pet owners as well as educational and consultation services to local animal clinics, animal welfare centers, military and K-9 personnel on the dynamics of the Human-Animal Bond and Pet Loss. I maintain a clinical practice that focuses on my role as a consultant, educator and author on the cultural evolution and importance of the Human-Animal Bond and impact of companion animal loss. My professional and personal interest in the Human-Animal Bond and Pet Loss was the inspiration for my Doctoral Dissertation research on the Human-Canine Bond entitled: *A Phenomenological Study of Canine Loss and Grief Response: Clinical and Depth Psychological Implications (2006).* This research investigated the relational dynamics that exist between humans and their canine companions and what the bereaved pet owner experiences when this bond is broken through death. Through my research, I explored the applicability of current models of human grief for this process and created a psychological model of grief specific to canine companion animal loss.

In addition to my work with the Human-Animal Bond and Pet Bereavement, I provide psychodynamic psychotherapy, mindfulness - based interventions and evidence-based treatment to adolescents and adults across the lifespan with specialized training and focus on; health psychology, chronic/ terminal illness, chronic pain syndrome, normative and traumatic life transitions, addictions, eating disorders and mood disorders.

Printed in Great Britain
by Amazon